Pop! Pop!

by Anne Schreiber and Gail Tuchman
Illustrated by Tony Griego

SCHOLASTIC

Pop! Pop on my log.

I like to pop on my log.

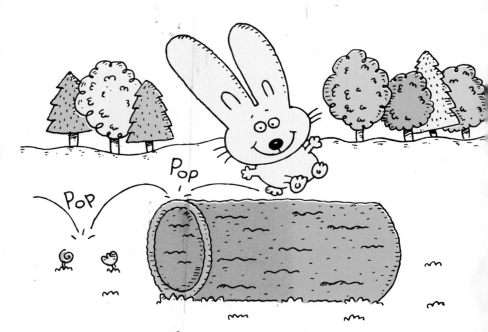

Tap! Tap on my log.

Who taps on my log?

Hop! Hop on my log.

Who hops on my log?

Mop! Mop on my log.

Who mops on my log?

Pit-Pat on my log.

Pop! Tap! Hop! Mop!

Pop! Pop in my log.

I like them in my log.

My Words

* in

* my

* them

Pp

pit-pat	mop
pop	mops
hop	tap
hops	taps

-og

log

*new high frequency words